Christ the Savior Is Born

Unto you is born this day in the city of David a Saviour. *Luke 2:11*

Written by **Tim Wesemann**

Illustrated by **Alex Steele-Morgan**

The vision of CTA is
to see Christians highly effective
in their ministry so that Christ's Kingdom
is strengthened and expanded.

Christ the Savior Is Born

Written by **Tim Wesemann**
Illustrated by **Alex Steele-Morgan**

Copyright © 2009, 2018 CTA, Inc.
1625 Larkin Williams Rd.
Fenton, MO 63026
www.CTAinc.com

The Scripture quotations are from the King James Version of the Bible.

Printed for CTA, Inc. Fenton, MO 63026 Printed in Bangpakong, Thailand
March 2018

ISBN 978-1-943216-84-0

The stars danced and twinkled
   in Bethlehem's sky,
Awaiting good news from the
   angels nearby.

Young Mary, with Joseph, felt time drawing near.
Both knew God the Father was leading them here.
They searched the whole town for a safe place to stay,
But all that they found was a stable with hay.
Although all alone and most likely afraid,
They clung to God's plan as they trusted and prayed.

At just the right time and in God's chosen place,
A newborn soon cried in his parents' embrace.
As bright stars shone down from the dark sky above,
Christ Jesus was born—he's the Gift of God's love.
Then Mary wrapped Jesus all snuggly and tight,
While angels in heaven rejoiced at the sight.

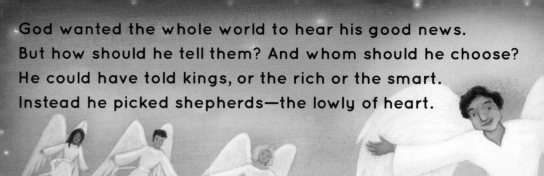

God wanted the whole world to hear his good news.
But how should he tell them? And whom should he choose?
He could have told kings, or the rich or the smart.
Instead he picked shepherds—the lowly of heart.

The Lord sent his angels to dark fields that night.
The shepherds fell down at the bright, holy sight!
The angels announced, "Do not fear! This is true:
Good news of great joy straight from heaven to you!

"Christ the Savior is born! Jesus the King!
Christ the Savior is born! Praises we sing!"
They glorified God and gave praise to his name,
While shepherds on earth joined in all the acclaim.

The shepherds found Jesus, as angels had said,
All swaddled and loved, and with hay for a bed.

They knelt down to worship, right there in that place,
Then left to tell all of God's wonderful grace.
And all were amazed at the news they were told
By these joyful shepherds, a story so bold.

Then out of the East, Wise Men came from afar.
They followed a big, bright, and beautiful star.
Gold, incense, and myrrh—at his feet they laid down
Their gifts for the King born in Bethlehem town.

They looked one last time at the Christ Child's sweet face
And saw there for certain the God of all grace.

They left then for home on a bright, starry night.
Perhaps they heard songs of God's angels in flight!

Christ the Savior is born! Jesus the King!
Christ the Savior is born! Praises we sing!

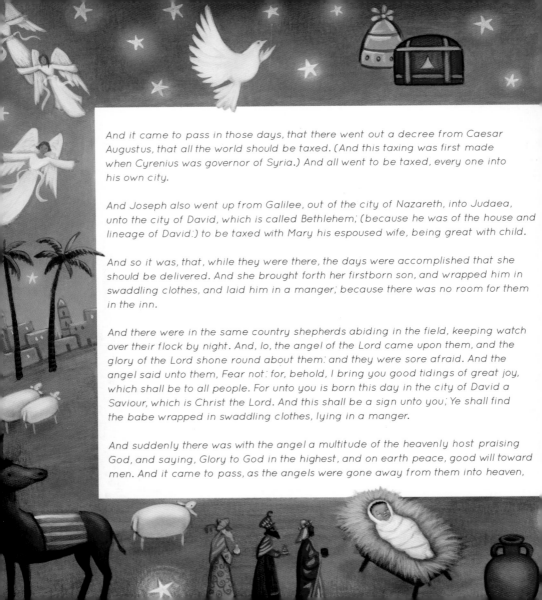

And it came to pass in those days, that there went out a decree from Caesar Augustus, that all the world should be taxed. (And this taxing was first made when Cyrenius was governor of Syria.) And all went to be taxed, every one into his own city.

And Joseph also went up from Galilee, out of the city of Nazareth, into Judaea, unto the city of David, which is called Bethlehem; (because he was of the house and lineage of David:) to be taxed with Mary his espoused wife, being great with child.

And so it was, that, while they were there, the days were accomplished that she should be delivered. And she brought forth her firstborn son, and wrapped him in swaddling clothes, and laid him in a manger; because there was no room for them in the inn.

And there were in the same country shepherds abiding in the field, keeping watch over their flock by night. And, lo, the angel of the Lord came upon them, and the glory of the Lord shone round about them: and they were sore afraid. And the angel said unto them, Fear not: for, behold, I bring you good tidings of great joy, which shall be to all people. For unto you is born this day in the city of David a Saviour, which is Christ the Lord. And this shall be a sign unto you; Ye shall find the babe wrapped in swaddling clothes, lying in a manger.

And suddenly there was with the angel a multitude of the heavenly host praising God, and saying, Glory to God in the highest, and on earth peace, good will toward men. And it came to pass, as the angels were gone away from them into heaven,

he shepherds said one to another, Let us now go even unto Bethlehem, and see his thing which is come to pass, which the Lord hath made known unto us. And they came with haste, and found Mary, and Joseph, and the babe lying in a manger.

And when they had seen it, they made known abroad the saying which was told hem concerning this child. And all they that heard it wondered at those things which were told them by the shepherds. But Mary kept all these things, and pondered them in her heart. And the shepherds returned, glorifying and praising God for all the things that they had heard and seen, as it was told unto them.

Luke 2:1-20

Now when Jesus was born in Bethlehem of Judaea in the days of Herod the king, behold, there came wise men from the east to Jerusalem, saying, Where is he that is born King of the Jews? for we have seen his star in the east, and are come to worship him.

Matthew 2:1-2

When they had heard the king, they departed; and, lo, the star, which they saw in the east, went before them, till it came and stood over where the young child was. When they saw the star, they rejoiced with exceeding great joy. And when they were come into the house, they saw the young child with Mary his mother, and fell down, and worshipped him: and when they had opened their treasures, they presented unto him gifts; gold, and frankincense, and myrrh.

Matthew 2:9-11

A Note to the Grown-Ups

Christ the Savior is born! What amazing news wrapped around a beautiful and intriguing story. A young, faith-filled couple. A small, unassuming town. An unusual birthing place, to say the least! Shepherds, totally lacking in status, receive the honor of visiting the newborn King. A multitude of heavenly host bringing the message. Improbable visitors—rich, Gentile stargazers. Unique in every way, it's a story we treasure because of the true Treasure named Jesus.

This book takes the reader through the Christmas story in rhyme, accompanied by stunning artwork that brings Bethlehem to life. As you read *Christ the Savior Is Born* with your family, allow the words and illustrations to bring the events surrounding Jesus' birth into your home in a special way.

Read and perhaps learn the theme verse by heart:

Unto you is born this day in the city of David a Saviour, which is Christ the Lord.

Luke 2:11

Included in these pages, you will also find the account of Jesus' birth, as recorded in Matthew 1 and Luke 2. As you read those words from the Bible, encourage family members to listen carefully and, perhaps, to commit other parts of the text to memory. God's Word, planted in each heart, will reap blessings for years to come.

May the joyous events that took place on Bethlehem's special night strengthen the faith of each member of your family. And may the news that Christ the Savior is born continue to make a life-changing difference in your lives throughout the New Year ahead.

Tim Wesemann